Previously on

TEAHOUSE

Hey again! You're back! Things have been kind of crazy around here, I have so much to tell you!

So Rhys came back with Mr. Tall! Turns out Mr. Tall is a lord or something! Lord Reed, how fancy is that? He's really picky about his wine glasses.

Oh yeah, and Rory didn't have sex.

But Axis did! Sounded like Rhys came to collect the freebie Axis owed him. There were a lot of... noises... coming from his room...

OH! And I heard Atros was giving Axis' room to Rory! Can you believe it? Rory's now the top earner! He must be really talented at... talking... or something not "sex!"

I hear Atros had a talk with that creepy Liard guy. I don't like his stupid face, I hope Atros told him to go away!

Mercutio ruined my favorite shoes, Lilith called me fat, Argent was super cool, and Linneus looked really pretty!

And now you know everything I know!

YOU'VE BEEN AVOIDING ME FOR A WEEK.
CLICK
ARE YOU STILL UPSET ABOUT LIARD?
...
OR IS THIS ABOUT THE OTHER NIGHT?

CLARET DOESN'T FLOURISH HER TRAYS WITH ROSES.
I KNOW IT WAS YOU.
YOU SHOULD LEARN HOW TO PROPERLY CLOSE A DOOR.
YOUR JEALOUSY IS UNNECESSARY. YOU KNOW MY DOOR IS JUST AS OPEN TO YOU AS IT IS TO LILITH.

THAT MAY BE, BUT I AM NOT YOUR PERSONAL WHORE!
MY WHORE IS EXACTLY WHAT YOU ARE!

I'VE SPENT THE LAST EIGHT YEARS WONDERING...
...IF "WHORE" WAS ALL YOU SAW WHEN YOU LOOKED AT ME.

THANK YOU FOR FINALLY CONFIRMING IT.

CLOSE THE DOOR.

—CLICK
GOD DAMMIT.

OH!
OMPH!
IT'S OK! I'M OK!
I'M SO SORRY! I WAS JUST IN A HURRY AND--
CLARET, YOU'RE HANDLING SCHEDULING NOW, RIGHT?
YEAH, ATROS SAID THAT IF I'M GOING TO BE A USELESS COURTESAN I MIGHT AS WELL DO SOMETHING THAT'S USEFU--
COULD YOU DO ME A FAVOR?
CANCEL MY APPOINTMENTS FOR THE DAY.
BUT ATROS WILL BE UPSE--
IF HE HAS A PROBLEM WITH IT, TELL HIM IT'S MY FAULT AND THAT I MADE YOU CANCEL THEM.
KISS
BUT!
THANKS, CLARET!
BUT...BUT LINNEUS!

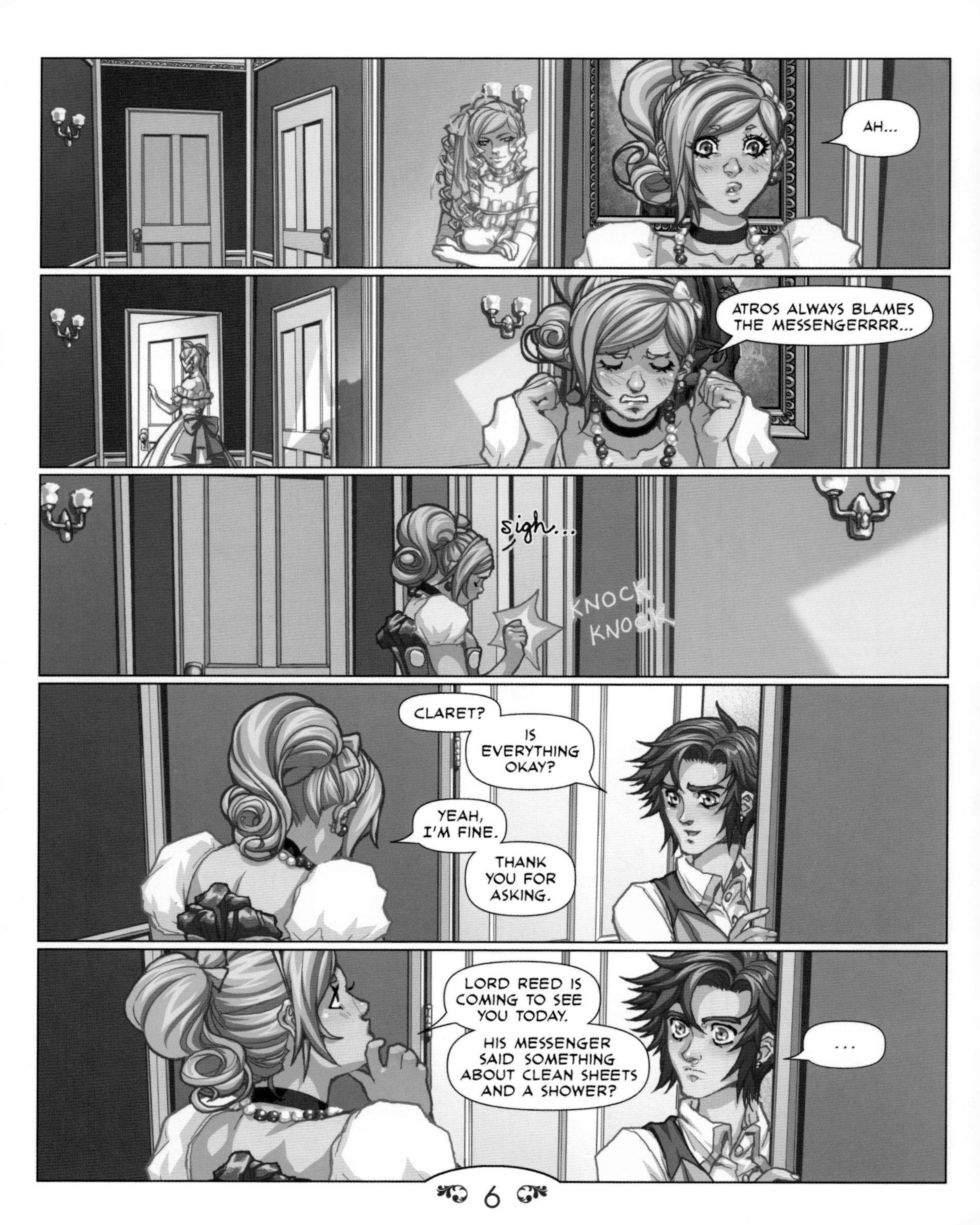
AH...
ATROS ALWAYS BLAMES THE MESSENGERRRR...
sigh...
KNOCK KNOCK
CLARET?
IS EVERYTHING OKAY?
YEAH, I'M FINE.
THANK YOU FOR ASKING.
LORD REED IS COMING TO SEE YOU TODAY.
HIS MESSENGER SAID SOMETHING ABOUT CLEAN SHEETS AND A SHOWER?
...

THEN THE DATE IS SET.
ONE MONTH FROM FRIDAY DOES NOT LEAVE US MUCH TIME TO PREPARE FOR A ROYAL WEDDING, BUT WE SHALL DO OUR BEST.
ARE YOU PREPARED FOR THE POSSIBILITY OF A CORONATION?
GOD WILLING, THE KING WILL LIVE TO SEE HIS ONLY SON MARRIED.
IT IS FOOLISH OF YOU TO ASSUME WHAT IS AND WHAT ISN'T GOD'S WILL, CHANCELLOR.
HOW DA--
IN REGARDS TO THE CORONATION...
FATHER HAS BEEN ILL FOR QUITE SOME TIME, YOU NEED NOT WORRY ABOUT OUR PREPAREDNESS IN THIS MATTER.

MY APOLOGIES FOR MY ABRUPT DEPARTURE, BUT IT SEEMS THAT I HAVE MUCH TO ATTEND TO WITH LITTLE TIME TO SPARE.

MAY I ESCORT YOU TO YOUR ROOM, YOUR GRACE?

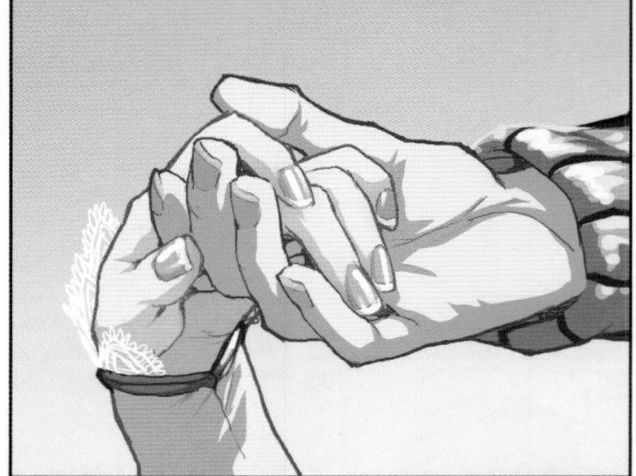

YOU'RE QUITE FAMOUS FOR YOUR CONQUESTS.
IS THAT SO? EVEN IN VERONE?

JUST SO WE'RE CLEAR, I DON'T CARE ABOUT WHO YOU'RE DEBASING...
...JUST AS LONG AS YOU'RE DISCREET ABOUT IT.

OF COURSE. WE CAN'T HAVE THE PLEBS DISCOVER OUR LOVE IS BULLSHIT, CAN WE, DARLING.
DO NOT TEST ME ON THIS.

I HAVE NOT SPENT MY ENTIRE LIFETIME GROOMING MYSELF TO BECOME QUEEN ONLY TO MARRY AN IDIOT...YOU WILL ACT ACCORDINGLY.

OR I WILL MAKE YOUR LIFE AND YOUR CUNT'S LIFE A LIVING HELL.

IT'S GOING TO BE A THRILL A MINUTE TRYING TO GET YOU PREGNANT.

I UNDERSTAND YOUR GRACE.

ZEPHYR.
WHAT ARE YOU DOING TO--
RHYS, WHAT IS THIS?
IT APPEARS TO BE THE BUSINESS CARD OF A BROTHEL, EVELYN.
I KNOW THAT! YOU LEFT THIS IN YOUR CARRIAGE!
ARE YOU SERIOUSLY GOING TO A BROTHEL NOW?!
CLICK
THEY'RE QUITE GOOD. YOU SHOULD GO, YOU'VE BEEN REALLY TENSE.
THIS IS **NOT** THE WAY A KING SHOULD CONDUCT HIMSELF, RHYS!
STOP WORRYING ABOUT ME AND TAKE CARE OF YOURSELF FOR A CHANGE, EVIE.
LEARN TO RELAX A LITTLE.
...

YOU SEEM DISTRACTED...

WHAT'S ON YOUR MIND, XA--

WHY DO I EVEN BOTHER ASKING?
YOU TWO ARE SO TRANSPARENT.

NONE OF THIS CONCERNS YOU.

HE CANCELLED ALL OF HIS APPOINTMENTS.
HE'S COSTING YOU MONEY--
LEAVE IT.

FUCKINHATESLOWDAYS...
ESPECIALLY WHEN IT MEANS I'M STUCK WITH JUST YOU.

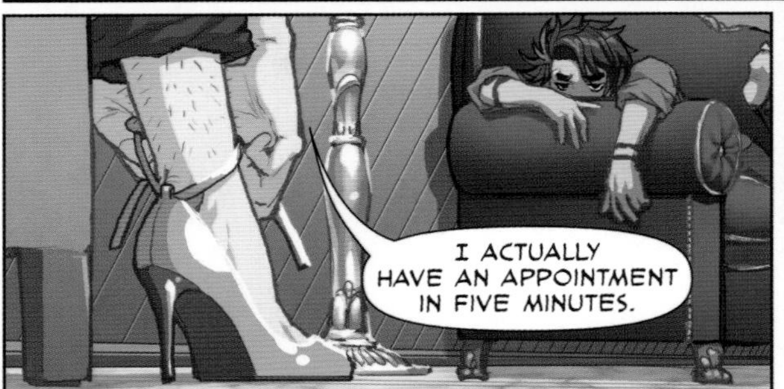
I ACTUALLY HAVE AN APPOINTMENT IN FIVE MINUTES.

click
CLARET'S SHOES FIT LIKE A DREAM, DON'T THEY?
NIGHTMARE.

HEY, LORD COCKBREATH, WHERE'S YOUR FANCY LITTLE SIDEKICK?

I THOUGHT HE'D BE MISSING ME BY NOW.
RHYS HAS FAR MORE IMPORTANT MATTERS TO ATTEND TO.

...

HE WAS JUST INSULTING ME, WASN'T HE?
HE MOST DEFINITELY WAS, DARLING.

KNOCK KNOCK

HI, I'VE BEEN...UM... WAITING FOR YOU.

NOT THAT...I MEAN...I WASN'T *WAITING* LIKE YOU'RE LATE OR ANYTHING LIKE THAT.

I MADE YOU CUPCAKES! AND I SHOWERED, LIKE YOU ASKED. I SORT OF RUSHED ON THE CUPCAKES, BUT...

EVERYONE SAID THEY STILL TASTE REALLY GOOD. WHICH I WAS WORRIED ABOUT BECAUSE--

BECAUSE... BECAUSE I WAS WORRIED AND BAKING IS SUCH AN EXACT--

MMMMFF!

GASP!

AH... IS THERE ANYTHING...
UH... I SHOULD BE...

AH!!

AH... THAT...THAT FEELS...
GASP
REALLY NIC--

MFFF.

Ha...

AH!

pant pant

gasp!

AH!

AH! AHHHH...
NNN...
NNNNNM.
L-LORD REED! I- I'M G--
I'M GOING TO--
GET IN THE TUB.

HOW HOT
WOULD YOU
LIKE THE WATER
TO BE?

WARM?
HO...

DO YOU FIND ME
DISPLEASING?
WHAT?
NO!

YOU'RE VERY
PLEASING--I MEAN
--YOU LOOK
PLEASING--
IT'S
JUST...I'M
JUST...

NERVOUS...

AH!
NNNM...
AHHHHH...
A-AHHHH!

L-LORD REED...
NNNH...
DO IT.
AH...
AHHHHHH!

I SAID TOO MUCH.

... A LINE WAS CROSSED.

creak

SO IT'S JUST THE TWO OF YOU?
FOR THE MOMENT, YES.
SERIOUSLY? NO OTHER LADIES?

WE HAVE OTHER MEN IF YOU'D LIKE TO--
WHAT ABOUT HER??

WHO, LINNEUS?
THAT'S A ***MAN.***
IT IS?

...ALRIGHT. SURE. WHY NOT?
LINNEUS!

MR. GILDER HERE WOULD LIKE TO HIRE YOU FOR THE EVENING!
JUST GILDER'S FINE, DOLL.

OH, BUT I'M NOT SE--

WHAT WAS THAT, DOVE?

IT'S NOTHING.

I'D LOVE TO.

I'M AFRAID YOU CAUGHT ME UNPREPARED.
IF YOU'LL EXCUSE ME FOR A MOMENT TO FRESHE--

YOU SMELL LIKE ROSES.

I JUST NEED A FEW MINUTES...

I PROMISE IT'LL BE WORTH THE WAIT.

I'D RATHER YOU DROP THE ACT, DOVE.

I THINK YOU'RE JUST FINE...

...LIKE THIS.

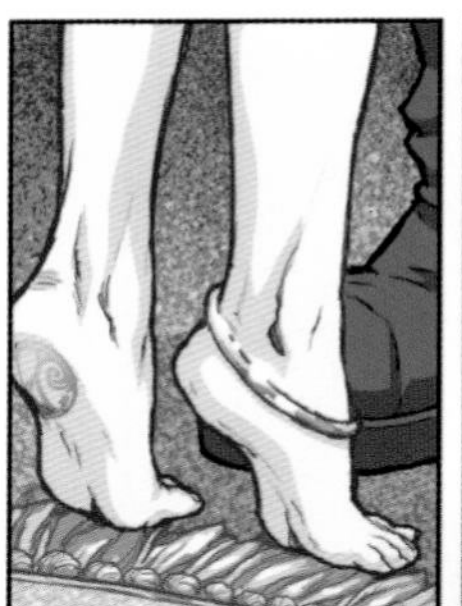
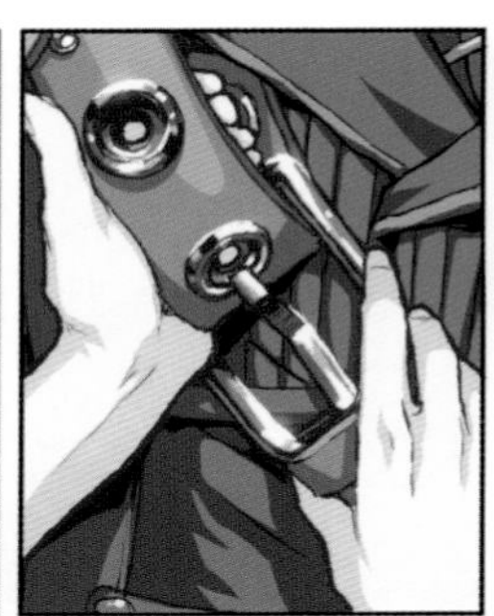

THUNK

shff

CLANK
CLINK
CLANK

WHAT'S...
WHY DO YOU...
SO MANY...

I UH... CUT TREES...
...AND STUFF...

...SO...

UH...
...DID YOU... WANT TO TELL ME ABOUT YOURSELF?

I AM AN ARMS DEALER AND I HAVE OCD.
...

WAIT!

I KNOW THEY'RE A BIT MESSY BECAUSE I WAS RUSHING AND--

I HAVE NO DESIRE FOR ANYTHING "RUSHED."
CREAK

RORY.

YOU ARE TOO TIGHT.

FIX THAT.

...

I...I DON'T KNOW.
I WAS JUST EXPECTING SOMEONE MORE... *REFINED.*

TRUST ME, WHEN YOU COME TO A PLACE LIKE THIS...

...*REFINED* ISN'T WHAT YOU WANT.

I GUESS THAT'S TRUE...

I PROMISE YOU WON'T REGRET IT, PRINCESS.

SO THIS REALLY USED TO BE A TEAHOUSE?
YEARS AND YEARS AGO.
MASTER ATROS SECRETLY CONVERTED IT INTO A BROTHEL BEFORE THEY WERE LEGALIZED.
I THOUGHT THE GUY WHO RAN THIS PLACE WAS MY AGE.
MASTER ATROS DIED EIGHT YEARS AGO.
HIS SON RUNS IT NOW.
WHAT?
YOU'RE REALLY BEAUTIFUL.

YOU ARE ENTIRELY TOO CHARMING.
BUT YOU ARE!

WHAT, NO ONE'S EVER TOLD YOU THAT BEFORE?
BEFORE AND DURING SEX, YES...

...BUT PRETENSES HAVE A TENDENCY TO DROP AFTERWARDS.
GEEZ, WHAT KINDA CLIENTS ARE YOU GETTING?

THEY'RE NOT ALL THAT BAD.
SO ONLY "MOST" OF THEM ARE UGLY OLD RICH PIGS?

THEY'RE DEFINITELY NOT YOU...BUT THEY TREAT ME DECENTLY AND THAT'S THE MOST I COULD HOPE FOR, REALLY.

EVER BEEN IN LOVE WITH ANY OF 'EM?

END OF
Chapter Three

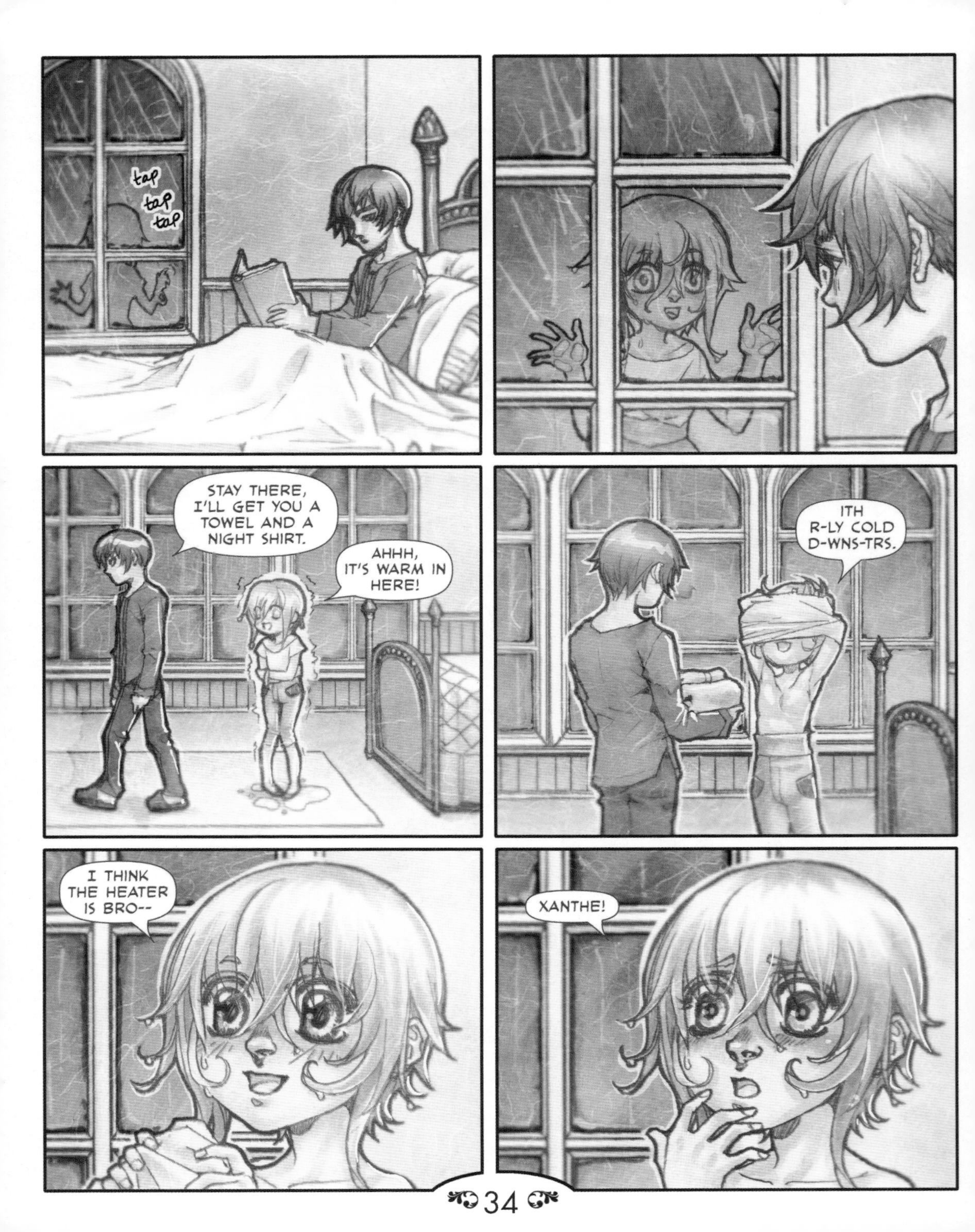
tap
tap
tap
STAY THERE, I'LL GET YOU A TOWEL AND A NIGHT SHIRT.
AHHH, IT'S WARM IN HERE!
ITH R-LY COLD D-WNS-TRS.
I THINK THE HEATER IS BRO--
XANTHE!

IT'S NOTHING.

WAS IT--

I SAID IT'S NOTHING.
ACK!

CHANGE. YOU'RE GETTING MY FLOOR ALL WET.

...
...WHAT'S WRONG?

...
FATHER'S SENDING ME AWAY.
XANTHE!

HE'S SENDING ME TO BOARDING SCHOOL.
HE SAID I NEED TO FOCUS ON MY EDUCATION.
...

I'LL WRITE YOU.

I'LL WRITE YOU EVERY DAY!

ONCE A WEEK IS ENOUGH!
I'LL HAVE HOMEWORK TO DO.

SO YOU'VE BEEN PRACTICING YOUR PENMANSHIP?
EVERYDAY!

GOOD, BECAUSE IF I CAN'T READ YOUR HAND WRI-

AHHHHHHAHAHAHAHAHAH AHAHAHAHAHAHAH!

WHAAAAT??
WHAT'S SO FUNNY!?!

OH YEAH!?
poomf!

YOU LOOK FUNNY WHEN MY PILLOW HITS Y--
KNOCK KNOCK KNOCK

WHAT'S GOING ON IN THERE?
NOTHING, FATHER. I WAS JUST READING MY BOOK ALOUD.

READ SILENTLY, YOU'RE NO LONGER A CHILD.
YES, FATHER.

WE SHOULD SLEEP.
click
YOU OK?

PROMISE YOU'LL WRITE ME ONCE A WEEK?
YEAH.

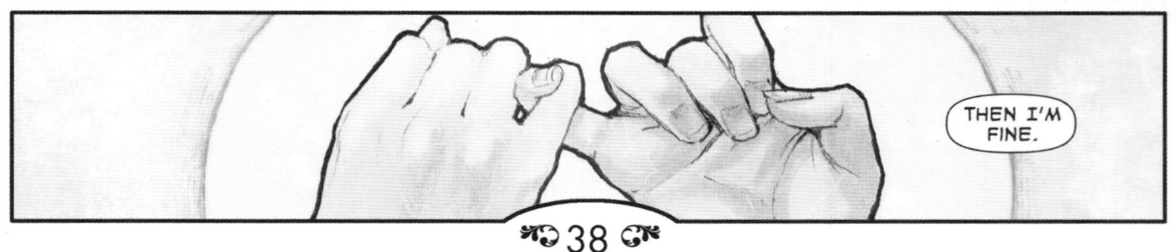
THEN I'M FINE.

ZZZ

WHAT'S THIS?

YOU REQUIRED TO DO A LITTLE EXTRA FOR YOUR OVERNIGHT GUESTS?

NO.

THIS ONE'S FOR ME.

NNN...
AH..
HAA...
AH!
NNM!

AHHH!

AHNN!

NGH!
AHHHHH!

IF YOU WAKE ME UP IN AN HOUR, I PROMISE I'LL LAST LONGER.
YOU WERE JUST SO SEXY... THIS TIME...

ZZZ

A Day in the Life of Mercutio
8:00 A.M.
9:00 A.M.
10:00 A.M.
SMACK
11:00 A.M.

12:00 P.M.

1:00 P.M.

2:00 P.M.

3:00 P.M.

4:00 P.M.
5:00 P.M.
MOOOO
6:00 P.M.

7:00 P.M.

SLURP
8:00 P.M.

9:00 P.M.

10:00 P.M.

11:00 P.M.

Printed by Transcontinental on November 28, 2012; Second Edition.

Story and Art EMIRAIN
Lettering MURRAY ALAMO
Flats & Colorholds ANNERS
Story Editor HAN LING
Production Artist FAWNFAWN

Special thanks to our awesomely supportive readers, because without you we wouldn't be able to spend so much time on this project. Thanks for the readership and support, and we hope you continue to enjoy Teahouse!

Continue reading Teahouse at
WWW. TEAHOUSECOMIC.COM